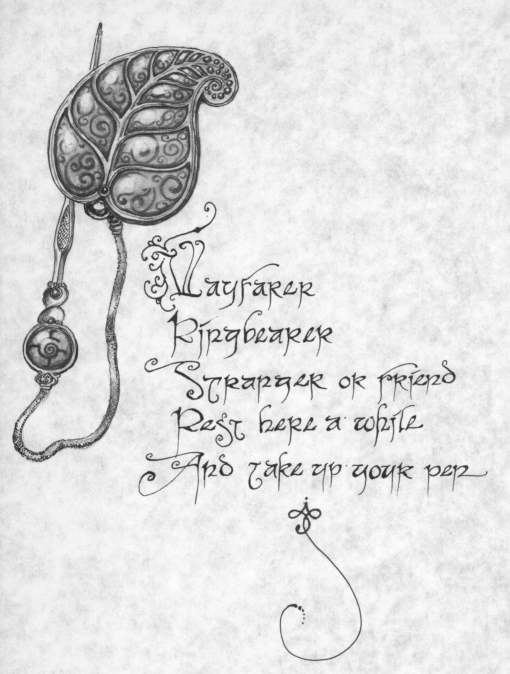

Wayfarer
Ringbearer
Stranger or friend
Rest here a while
And take up your pen

The long wait of Arwen Evenstar

A HOBBIT'S JOURNAL

Mayor Gamgee

In the fullness of his years, Master Samwise, thrice mayor of the Shire, and last of the Ringbearers, took to mind the words of Frodo—that it would be his task to complete the narrative of the great War of the Rings. Being a practical hobbit, he realized that simple drawings save many words, but when he set his hand to the task, the craft of capturing a likeness eluded him. Remembering that many skillfull artisans had gathered to the court of Minas Tirith, he sent there word of his need. Scarcely two moons had grown full when there appeared at the gates of the Shire one Michael the Green, King's Illuminator. Many days the two spent, Sam and Michael, hobbit and man, strolling the byways of the Shire, or sitting by a crackling fire. While Sam described the remarkable adventure Michael's pen brought it to life. Eventually, several folios of drawings were completed, each page leaving room for the hobbit to write his stories. But the final work, it is told, filled Sam with such delight that he could never bring himself to mark the pages. Now some of these folios have been lovingly reproduced in this handy journal so that you, Dear Reader, can herein write your part of the story. There is only one hero, he has a thousand faces. One of them is yours.

Bilbo Baggins, who Started it all

Gandalf

Sam Gamgee and Friend

Peregrin Took

Merriadoc,
Sometime
Door-warder
of Isengard

Aragorn son of Arathorn

Legolas Greenleaf

Gimli son of Gloin

BOROMIR

Bombadil

Another daughter of the River King

Retreat from Caradhras

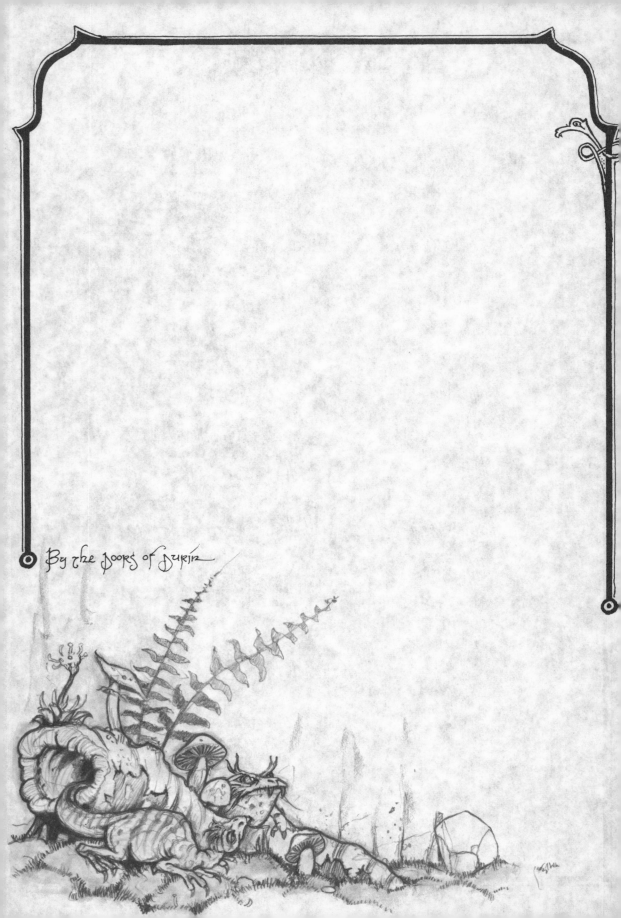

By the Doors of Durin

Glamdring

The Lady of the Wood

Éomer
son of Éomund

Éomer's Tale

Treebeard

Another notch
for Gimli's ax

The seige of Helm's Deep

Shield-maiden of Rohan

The Palantir is taken

Faramir

Elrohir son of Elrond

War-horse of Rohan

Ghân-buri-Ghân

The Darkness of Derethor

The trial of Gondor

The last ride of Théoden King

The
Black Ships

March to the Morannon

I am the
Mouth of
Sauron

The White Crown

The Gaffer

Farmer Cotton
and son